Contents

Special Features

Features

Microbes

Written by Brian Roberts

Every day of your life, you face many dangers. You could be hit by a car. You could fall off a bike or be struck by lightning. Or there are thousands of other things that can cause you harm. Most of these dangers are obvious. But perhaps some of the greatest dangers cannot be seen. These dangers are caused by an unseen world of living things called microbes. Some microbes are unseen killers and cause millions of deaths each year to humans and other animals. These harmful microbes are commonly called germs.

But not all microbes are bad. Some of them are quite useful. We could not live without them.

So, understanding microbes is important. In fact, our survival may depend on it.

Types of Microbes

Microbes are too small to be seen by the naked eye. Therefore, scientists use powerful microscopes to study them. For this reason, microbes are often called microscopic organisms.

There are thousands of different kinds of microbes. Some of them are beneficial. Others are harmful and cause disease. Doctors call microbes that cause disease pathogens. Some of the symptoms of pathogens infecting your body are fever, pain, nausea, tiredness, rashes, and inflammation. There are four main types of microscopic pathogens. They are bacteria, viruses, protozoa, and fungi. Let us take a closer look at each type of pathogen.

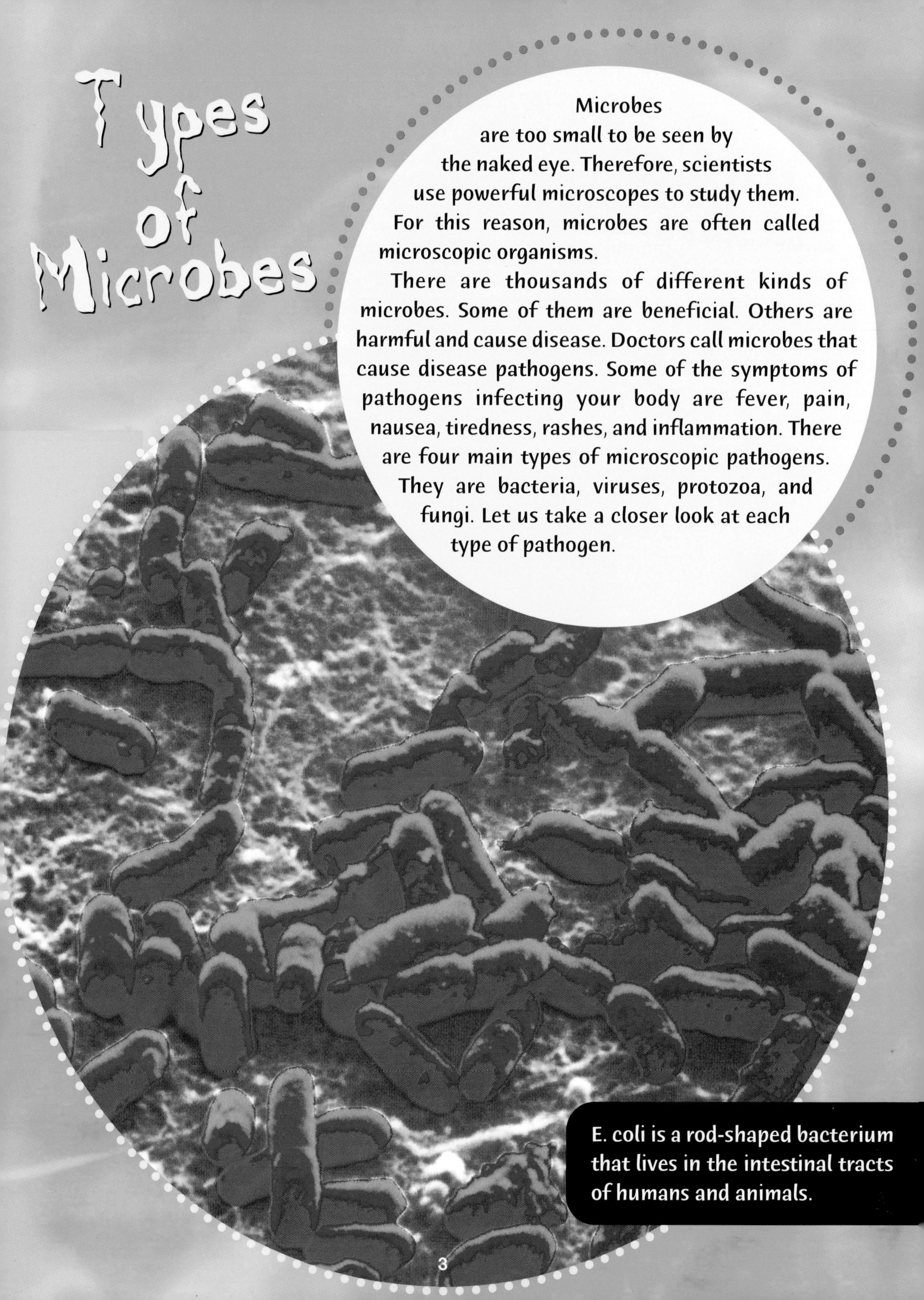

E. coli is a rod-shaped bacterium that lives in the intestinal tracts of humans and animals.

Bacteria

(singular: bacterium)

Tetanus, pneumonia, cholera, tuberculosis, and strep throat are only a few of the human diseases caused by bacteria.

Bacteria are tiny organisms made of a single cell. A unit of length called a micron (or, one millionth of a meter) is used to measure bacteria. Thousands of bacteria could fit on the dot of an *i*. But not all bacteria are pathogens. In fact, many bacteria are very good for us. We even use bacteria to make cheese and yogurt. Harmful bacteria, however, are responsible for many diseases and infections in the bodies of plants and animals.

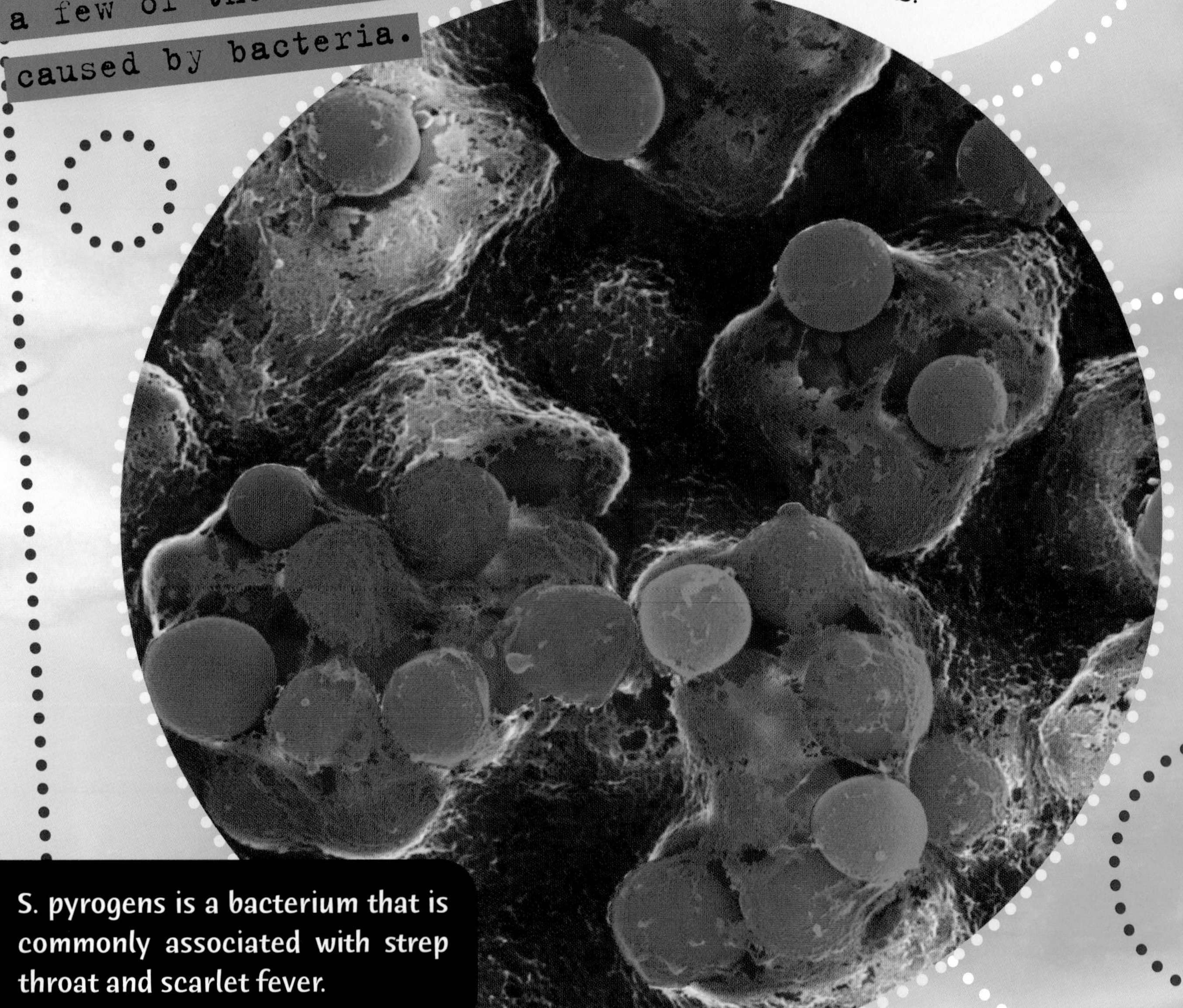

S. pyrogens is a bacterium that is commonly associated with strep throat and scarlet fever.

Viruses

(singular: virus)

If you think bacteria are small, consider viruses. They are ten to hundreds of times smaller than bacteria. But unlike bacteria, viruses do not even have a single cell. Viruses cannot reproduce unless they are inside the cell of another living thing. But, once a virus enters a cell, it takes over. It then makes the cell produce new viruses. Cells release the new viruses and these viruses then invade other cells. In a very short time, viruses can spread throughout the body and infect millions of other cells. An invasion by a virus can leave the body weak and diseased.

Some of the more common virus-caused diseases are mumps, measles, rabies, AIDS, and polio. Viruses also cause some cancers.

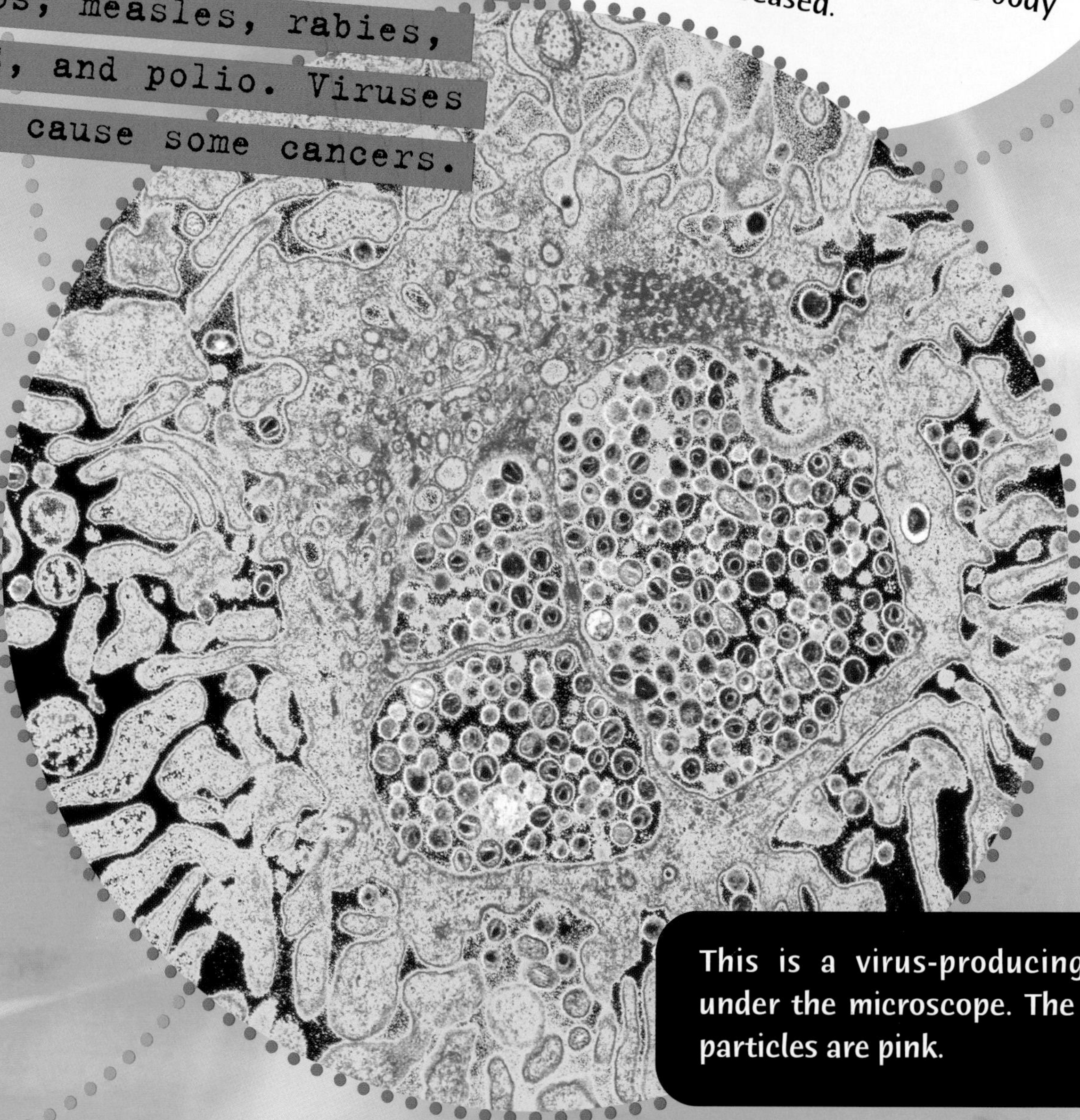

This is a virus-producing cell under the microscope. The virus particles are pink.

Protozoa

(singular: protozoan)

Protozoa are larger than bacteria, but they are still tiny single-cell organisms. They like to live where there is a lot of moisture. One of the most dangerous protozoa is one that causes malaria. These protozoa are carried by mosquitoes. If a mosquito carrying these malaria protozoa bites a human, the human can easily become infected with malaria. Each year, over two million people in the world die from malaria. That is equal to the population of a large city, or two-thirds the population of a country like New Zealand.

Fungi

(singular: fungus)

Fungi are often microscopic organisms, but some fungi, such as mushrooms, are easily visible. Fungi get their food by eating living or dead organic matter. Some microscopic fungi are parasites that live on the outside of human skin. These fungi cause conditions such as ringworm and athlete's foot. Other fungi can get inside the body and attack healthy tissue.

Many kinds of fungi produce important antibiotics, such as penicillin. Some other kinds of fungi are used to make cheese.

Where Microbes Are

Microbes are everywhere. They are where it is hot and where it is cold. They are where it is dry and where it is wet. They are in the water we drink. They are carried on dust particles in the air that we breathe. They are in and on the food we eat. They are on doorknobs and tables. And they are on almost any other surface you can think of.

Since microbes are tiny, it is easy for them to move around from place to place. That is why it is so easy for diseases to spread from one person to another person. For example, a virus that causes the common cold can be carried on moisture droplets that leave an infected person's body when they cough or sneeze.

Cold viruses get on the hand of a person who covers their mouth when they cough or sneeze. Then when they touch an object such as a doorknob, the viruses are left on the knob. When someone else touches the knob, the germs get on their hands. If they eat something before they have washed their hands, the cold viruses enter the body. They run the risk of catching a cold.

Other pathogens hitch rides aboard biting insects. Fleas, ticks, and mosquitoes are biting insects that carry pathogens. When an insect bites a person who is infected and then bites someone else, it passes the pathogen from person to person.

Protection Against Microbes

You might think that with microbes all around, you do not have a chance to escape the harmful ones. It is true that, sooner or later, some microbes will enter your body. And it is true that they might cause a problem. That problem could be a minor cold or a serious life-threatening disease.

Your body has several ways to defend itself from harmful microbes or pathogens. The first line of defence is your skin. Except for a few holes here and there, the skin is designed to keep harmful microbes out. Open wounds on the skin are like welcome mats for nasty microbes. That is why it is a good idea to keep open wounds covered and to apply a microbe-killing medicine to a wound.

Even the openings in your skin have ways of keeping microbes out. Your eyes produce tears to wash away foreign objects. Tears contain a protein that kills germs. Your ears have tiny hairs and wax to keep germs out. Tiny hairs and mucous membranes line your throat and nose. The mucous membranes secrete mucus that traps germs. This stops the germs from entering your body.

The last line of defence is your immune system. The immune system is made of microscopic defenders. The defenders attack pathogens that enter your body. Perhaps the most important defenders in your immune system are the white blood cells. They patrol your body by moving around in your blood. When they find a foreign object, they attack it. First, they surround it. Then they break it down and digest it.

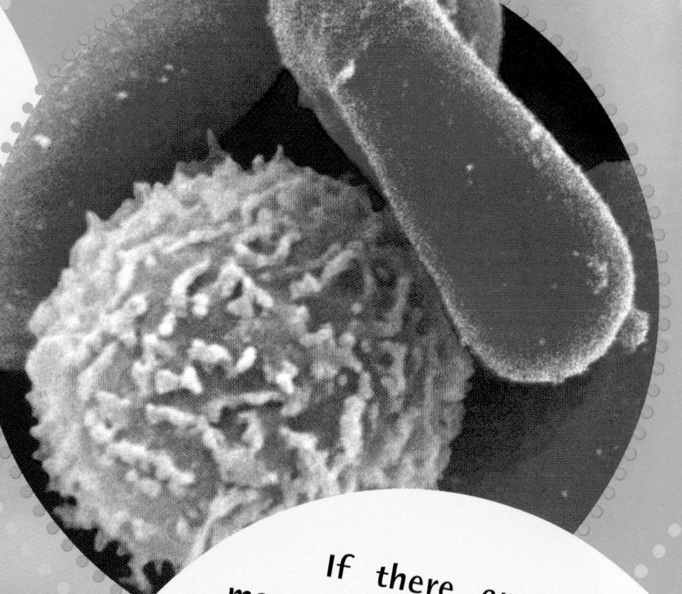

White blood cells are the body's primary defence system.

If there are too many invaders for the white blood cells to destroy, they get help from other defenders called antibodies. Antibodies are designed to attack specific foreign substances called antigens. Antigens that enter the body are first identified by special white blood cells. These are known as B-cells. The B-cells find and tag the antigen. Once the antigen is tagged, an antibody called a T-cell comes along and destroys it.

If the body's natural defences fail to stop the invading pathogens, it is time to get outside help. That help can come from medicine given by a doctor. One type of medicine is an antibiotic. Antibiotics can be put into your body with an injection, a pill, or as a liquid. The antibiotics then are carried throughout your body in the blood. Antibiotics attack antigens.

Safari POWER Choose a, b, or c?

Word Meanings

beneficial
a — *exciting*
b — *harmful*
c — *good*

invasion
a — *attack*
b — *retreat*
c — *flight*

monitored
a — *leaked*
b — *jumped*
c — *watched*

multiplying
a — *increasing*
b — *decreasing*
c — *staying the same*

organism
a — *mineral*
b — *animal*
c — *manufactured*

overpower
a — *overcome*
b — *surrender*
c — *yield*

perimeter
a — *stethoscope*
b — *edge*
c — *monocle*

recuperate
a — *decline*
b — *recover*
c — *deteriorate*

regular
a — *usual*
b — *extraordinary*
c — *random*

reliable
a — *dependable*
b — *fickle*
c — *irresponsible*

simultaneous
a — *at the same time*
b — *at different times*
c — *at fast speeds*

terrain
a — *knot*
b — *drain*
c — *ground*

Answers on page 21

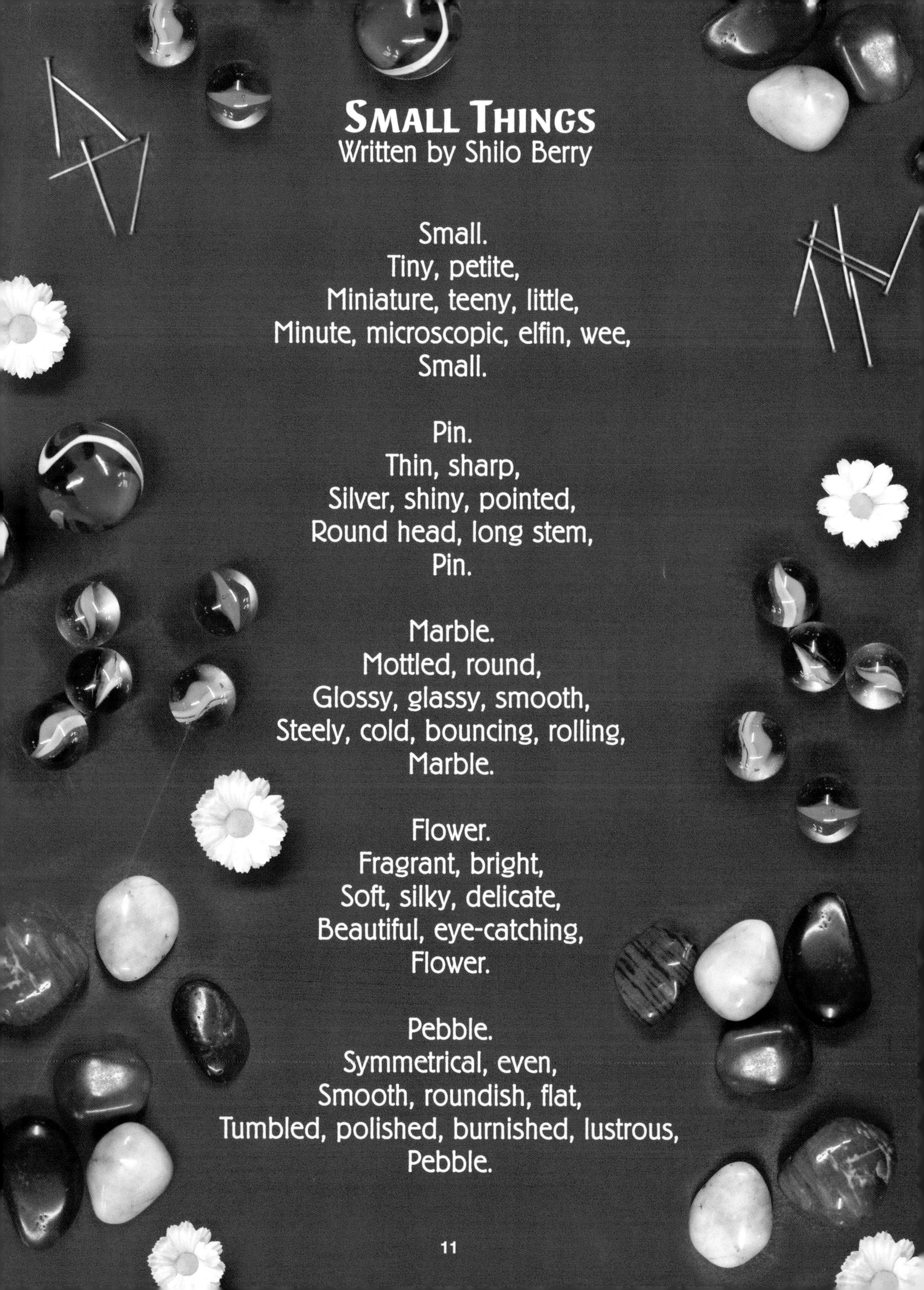

Small Things

Written by Shilo Berry

Small.
Tiny, petite,
Miniature, teeny, little,
Minute, microscopic, elfin, wee,
Small.

Pin.
Thin, sharp,
Silver, shiny, pointed,
Round head, long stem,
Pin.

Marble.
Mottled, round,
Glossy, glassy, smooth,
Steely, cold, bouncing, rolling,
Marble.

Flower.
Fragrant, bright,
Soft, silky, delicate,
Beautiful, eye-catching,
Flower.

Pebble.
Symmetrical, even,
Smooth, roundish, flat,
Tumbled, polished, burnished, lustrous,
Pebble.

BATTLE OF THE Bacteria BRIGADE

Written by Chantelle Greenhills
Illustrated by Shane Nagle

Wednesday Evening

Scott was feeling sick. His ears were sore and his head was pounding. It was as if someone was playing the drums right on top of him.

His nose was first blocked and then running faster than a mountain stream.

His throat felt like he had been trying to swallow glass.

Little did he know that an army of bacteria was beginning an attack on his body, and his immune system was trying to fight them off.

Tuesday – One Day Before

General Germ was standing in front of a table holding a pointer. He was looking at a large map that strongly resembled a human head.

Several germ colonels were surrounding him at the table.

"This is no straightforward attack," General Germ explained as he pointed to three positions on the map. "We will need to make several simultaneous attacks at these crucial points. Colonel Gerald, you and your troops will attack this top region. The terrain is very difficult in that area. The jungle is thick and dark. Your troops will need to spread out and move in through the caves on either side."

"Right, sir," responded Colonel Gerald Germ.

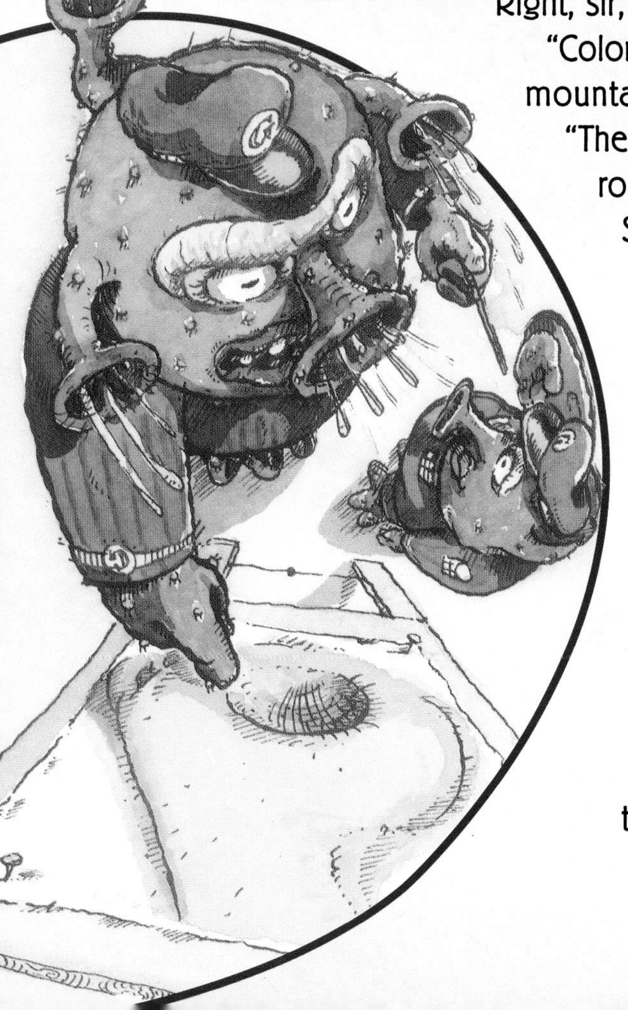

"Colonel Graham, you and your troops will attack this mountainous area here," continued the General. "The terrain in this area is unpredictable. Sometimes it is rough and rocky. Sometimes it is smooth and slimy. Sometimes it is blocked completely. There is no telling ahead of time what the conditions are like, so you will need to be prepared for all contingencies. Do I make myself clear?"

"Yes, indeed," replied Colonel Graham Germ.

"Colonel Glenda," General Germ continued, "you and your troops will attack this swampy gully region. It's a difficult spot, only one way in and the same way out. You will need to keep the path out clearly monitored so you don't get trapped. Do you understand?"

"Perfectly, sir," replied Colonel Glenda Germ.

"Good!" exclaimed General Germ. "Be prepared to begin moving out at 0800 hours tomorrow."

Four Hours Later, in Another Place Close By

"I'm glad you were all available at such short notice for this telecommunications conference," General Phagocyte told the good guys in Scott's immune system. "I didn't want to pull you away from your usual posts, as you need to be on full alert at all times, but we have recently received word from a reliable source that the Bacteria Brigade is planning several simultaneous attacks. We have no specific time for the attacks, so you will need to ready your troops and be prepared. I will send out defense plans via e-mail. Let me know the minute something happens in your area. Understood?"

"Yes, Sir, understood," replied the Phagocytes in unison.

"They certainly chose a good time to mount an attack," General Phagocyte continued, "with many of our troops still away at the bottom of the peninsula fighting the invasion at Cutty Knee. But right now we need everyone on stand-by back up here."

"Some of my troops are still recovering after the last attack," Phagocyte Phil said in a matter-of-fact way. "We are not back to full strength yet. We'll be all right if they attack through the jungle, but it'll be hard for us to repel an attack on the perimeter. Germs could quickly and easily get into the caves right now."

"I think the Bacteria Brigade are counting on the fact that our numbers are low," replied the General. "They've tried to attack many times before and every time they've been unable to overpower us. So this time they're trying to get us when we're down. All we can do is our best."

"We should be fine down here," answered Phagocyte Fred. "Our entrances are blocked. We need to do some maintenance work, but I'll hold off if we are expecting an attack. I think the germs would find it very difficult to get in and set the streams running under these conditions. So perhaps we could lend a hand elsewhere and leave just a few troops to keep guard here."

"Good idea," General Phagocyte agreed. "You know your area best. Leave a few troops and make your way over to Phagocyte Phil's perimeter area. You can help stop the germs getting into the caves. Have you anything to report, Flora?"

"We have bad conditions here in the swampy region," replied Phagocyte Flora into her telephone. "That should make it very difficult for outsiders to get through. And of course, the interior is slippery."

Wednesday, 0800 Hours

"Move out!" General Germ instructed his troops. "We need to make good time. As soon as you are in position, radio in, and then wait for the next instructions."

The 8,000-strong Bacteria Brigade made its way into position.

"Working double time is wearing me out," moaned a germ named Private Gavin.

"Yeah, me too," agreed his friend Private Gerico. "By the time we get there, I'll have no strength left at all. It sounds like a good idea to attack the phagocytes soon after the last attack, so we can catch them while they are still trying to recuperate, but the bosses forget that we need time to recuperate as well. When I make colonel, I'm going to think about those sorts of things."

"Remember last time? All that thick bushy jungle at the top of the peninsula? No wonder we didn't succeed. It was almost impossible to find a way through," Private Gavin said. "I wonder what the plan of action is going to be this time."

"I'm not sure, but I hope it's better than last time," Private Gerico responded. "I guess we'll be told when the time comes."

So the two soldiers marched on, worn out and breathing heavily, but keeping in time with their fellow germs.

Wednesday, 0800 hours, in Another Place Not Far Away

"How long have we been sitting here for now?" a front-line phagocyte asked.

"About five hours, I think," replied her friend. "Seems much longer, though."

"Do you think they will really attack again so soon after the last attack failed?" the first phagocyte asked.

"Maybe," replied the second phagocyte. "It's just like them to think they could catch us off guard. But they must be as tired as we are, and they have all that way to walk before they even start the attack, so I guess they won't attack for a while yet."

But she was wrong. On the signal from General Germ, the Bacteria Brigade struck.

The Battle of Bushy Jungle

Bacteria led by Colonel Gerald Germ launched their attack on Bushy Jungle. They attacked mostly around the perimeter, trying to gain access through the caves on either side of the thick jungle. The battle was long and hard-fought. Sometimes the germs appeared to have the upper hand; other times the Phagocytes did.

Meanwhile, Scott's ears were sore and his head was pounding like the drums in a rock band!

The Battle of Streaming Mountain

Phagocyte Fred had been right about the entrances to Streaming Mountain being blocked. But the germs were smart. Some shimmied up the side of the caverns and climbed along the roof until they were able to land behind the blockage. Then they were able to start the streams flowing. The phagocyte troops fell into position to confront the germs as they swung from the roof, but their numbers were small and the battle waged for a long time.

Meanwhile, Scott's nose was running faster than a mountain stream.

The Battle of Swampy Gully

The phagocytes were ready for the attack when it came, but they were still not able to beat off the attack before swarms of bacteria had crossed the slimy swamp and rushed down into the gravelly gully. Both sides fought well; the numbers and skills of the soldiers were closely matched.

Meanwhile, Scott's throat felt like he had eaten shredded glass.

Germ Retreat

The germs had attacked with such skill and swiftness that they had managed to surprise the vigilant phagocytes. The battles had been tough and both sides were weary. But the phagocytes were slowly starting to gain control. Halfway through the third night, General Germ realized that his side was losing, and gave the order to retreat. The germs were defeated again.

The phagocytes were exhausted, but they had done their job. They had protected their territory from the invaders.

Next morning, Scott woke up feeling much better.

Fax: Page 1 of 2

Flea Protest

I'm a flea and I want to protest the unfair treatment that we fleas as a species receive. We are constantly under threat from powders and sprays that have the sole purpose of exterminating us. What's a flea to do? We just want to go quietly about our business, like other creatures.

Fax: Page 2 of 2

After all, how much harm do fleas cause? Just a few itchy bites, that's all. And yet some people refuse to have a single flea in the house!

I'm sure that if you ask your pets, they'll tell you that they don't mind playing host to a few fleas.

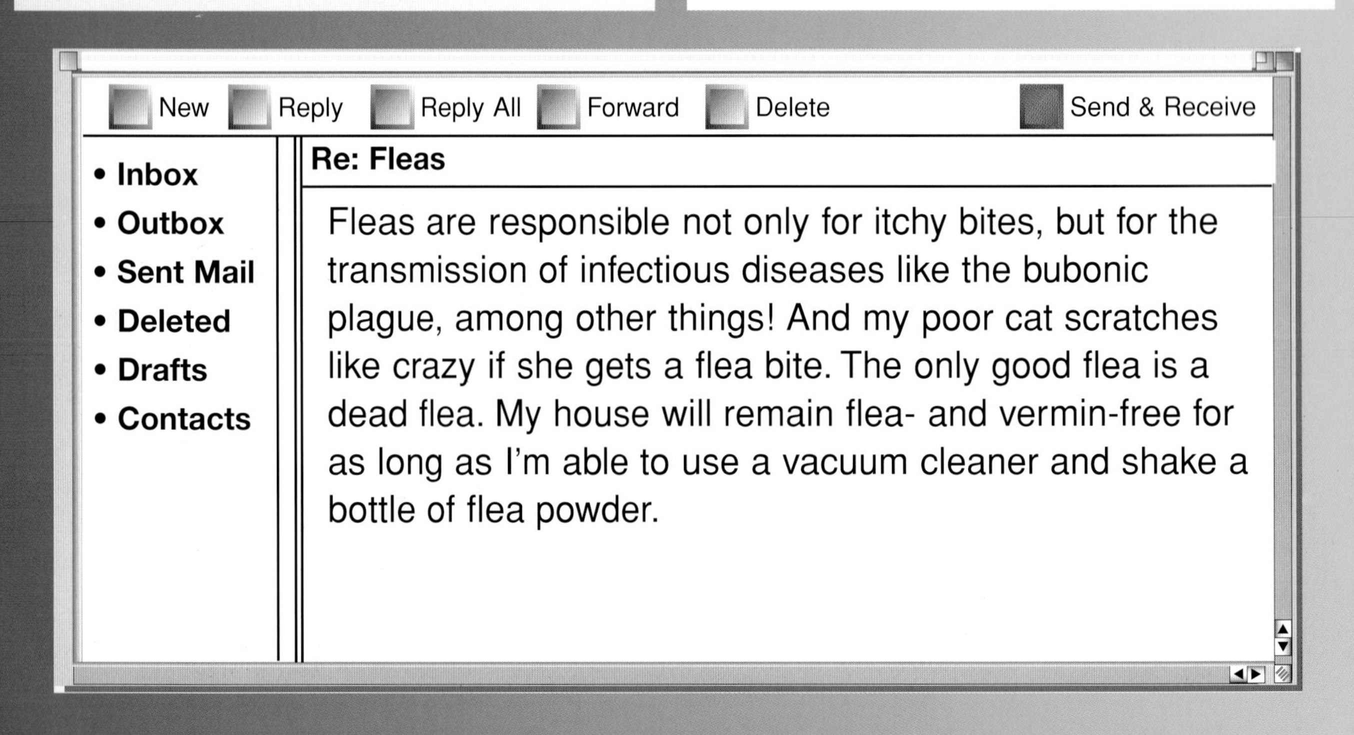

Safari POWER

Answers

beneficial
c – *good*

perimeter
b – *edge*

invasion
a – *attack*

recuperate
b – *recover*

regular
a – *usual*

monitored
c – *watched*

reliable
a – *dependable*

multiplying
a – *increasing*

simultaneous
a – *at the same time*

organism
b – *animal*

terrain
c – *ground*

overpower
a – *overcome*

a b c

Rating Scale

10-12 Excellent 7-9 Very good 4-6 Good 0-3 Try again

Xtra for Xperts

What is a pathogen?

FLEA ATTACK

Written by Veronica Angel

Characters

Flea 1

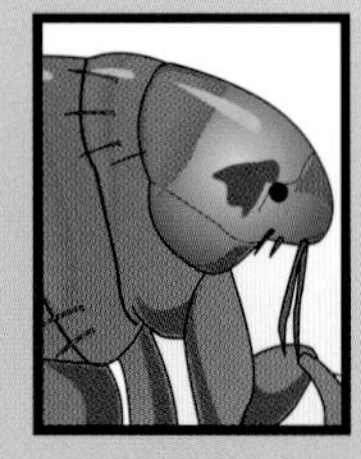

Flea 2

Giacomo

Mark

Narrator

Verona

SETTING

Giacomo and Verona's house.
Giacomo and Verona are away.

SCENE 1

Narrator
Two fleas are lying in their cocoons, waiting for the right moment to hatch. They are discussing the ups and downs of not having a ready supply of food.

Flea 1
Do you know how much longer they're going to be away?

Flea 2
No idea. But before they went, I heard them talking about being away for two months.

Flea 1
Well, they've been gone that long. Did you hear where they were going?

Flea 2
Overseas somewhere – Italy, I think.

Flea 1
Maybe they went to see their relatives in Italy.

Flea 2
I don't know. Where they are doesn't matter. What I want to know is what did they do with the dog?

Flea 1
They put it in the kennel.

Flea 2
That makes sense. They wouldn't want to take a dog to Italy for two months. It would be a lot of trouble.

Flea 1
I do wish they'd arranged for someone to come in and look through the house while they're gone. If it wasn't for the cat next door occasionally coming through the old cat door, we'd starve.

Flea 2
You're not the only one who needs a meal. I'm fed up with being in this cocoon. I want to get out and lay my eggs. It's very warm in here and they will hatch quickly.

Flea 1
Look, we'll be fine as soon as we feel the vibration in the floor that tells us they're back. They'll have the dog with them, and then we can have a meal.

Flea 2
I know. Hopefully, by the time they get back there'll be thousands of us. In 30 days, 10 females like us can multiply to over a quarter million. These conditions are ideal.

Flea 1
Then there's all the blind larvae. It will only take a week or so in this heat for them to mature, too. It's time they spun themselves into cocoons.

Flea 2
Yes, there'll be plenty of food for the larvae. All that dead skin and hair, not to mention the blood from our droppings. You're right. There really will be thousands of us in no time at all.

Flea 1
Well, it must only be a few days before they are back.

Flea 2
I can't wait.

SCENE 2

Narrator
Giacomo and Verona have returned from Italy. They drive straight to the kennels to pick up the dog.

Giacomo
It's really good to be home again, isn't it, Verona?

Verona
You know I love it when we travel back to Italy to see our parents; but I agree with you, there's no place like home.

Giacomo
How do you think Florence has been? Do you think she's missed us? I feel really bad about leaving her for so long, but it couldn't be helped with your mother sick.

Verona
Florence will be just fine. You know how much she likes coming to stay at the kennel. They all make such a fuss over her. And there are plenty of other dogs for her to play with.

Giacomo
But do you think she'll remember us? We've never been away this long before.

Verona
Just wait till she sees us. She'll be jumping all over us. Here she comes with Mark now.

Giacomo
Come here, Florence! Good girl!

Narrator
The dog comes bounding over.

Mark
She's been very well behaved. She loves it here, don't you, Florence?

Giacomo
It's good to know that she's so well cared for when we're away. But it's even better to see that she remembers us!

Verona
She smells good. Has she just had a bath?

Mark
She sure has. We bathe and groom the dogs every day.

Giacomo
Thanks, Mark.

SCENE 3

Narrator
Giacomo and Verona return to the house with Florence.

Giacomo
The house smells really musty after being shut for so long.

Verona
We really should have asked Agnes to come in once a week and open the windows for a while. Never mind. Everything looks fine.

Flea 1
They're here!

Flea 2
Finally! I was getting worried. Now we can have a meal!

Flea 1
I hope the dog hasn't had a bath for a while.

Flea 2
Or had flea powder applied.

Flea 1
I'll go have a quick look.

Narrator
Two minutes later the flea is back from Florence's body.

Flea 1
There's some old flea powder on her, but I'm pretty sure it won't have an effect on us.

Flea 2
OK then. I'm so hungry I'm willing to risk it. Shall we do it?

Flea 1
Yeah. I'm going to jump. Here goes!

SCENE 4

Narrator
The next day is hot and Florence looks very uncomfortable.

Verona
Florence seems to be scratching a lot today.

Giacomo
Stop it, Florence. Stop that scratching. You had a bath at the kennel yesterday. You shouldn't need to scratch like that.

Verona
She's not stopping. Maybe she has a rash or something. We'd better have a look, Giacomo.

Giacomo *(amazed)*
She's covered in fleas! She must have picked them up at the kennel.

Verona
I think you should telephone Mark to complain.

Giacomo
I agree.

Narrator
Giacomo goes to the telephone and dials the number of the kennel.

Mark
Hello, this is Pets' Paradise. You're talking to Mark.

Giacomo
Mark, Giacomo here. We have a serious problem.

Mark
How can I help?

Giacomo
It's Florence.

Mark
What's the matter with her?

Giacomo
Florence is covered in fleas. We think she must have picked them up at the kennel. But you said you groomed and bathed the animals every day. How can this happen? Did she catch the fleas from another dog?

Mark
No, she didn't get the fleas here. We don't have any place where fleas can breed. And we put a special chemical in the bath water to kill any fleas that the dogs bring in with them. She must have picked them up at your house.

Giacomo *(horrified)*
Are you suggesting that our house has fleas?

Mark
No, but I know that no other dogs here have fleas, and we haven't had any other complaints.

Giacomo
I don't believe you. We certainly won't be using your kennel again!

Narrator
He slams down the phone.

Verona
What's the matter, Giacomo? What did he say?

Giacomo
He said that Florence must have caught the fleas here.

Verona
That's ridiculous!

Giacomo
I know. He said that there was no way she got them at the kennel. What a dreadful thing to say! I told him we would never take Florence there again.

Verona
Well, we'd both better calm down. Let's go downtown straight away and buy some flea powder. That'll fix it. Then we'll come home and give Florence a good bath and put the flea powder on her.

SCENE 5

Narrator
Giacomo and Verona leave Florence in the house and go to buy the flea powder.

Flea 1
Did you hear that? They're going to town to get some of that dreadful flea powder.

Flea 2
I guess we'll just have to get our meals from Verona and Giacomo for a while.

Flea 1
I'm going to start jumping just as soon as they get back.

Flea 2
I think we will all be doing that, or the flea powder will kill us.

SCENE 6

Narrator
Giacomo and Verona return with the flea powder. They dust Florence with it thoroughly. But the next day, bumps start appearing on their skin.

Verona
Oh my goodness! Look at my ankles. *I'm* covered in flea bites! This is terrible!

Giacomo
The fleas must be multiplying. This is terrible. They can't just be on Florence anymore. They must be in all the carpets and the furniture by now. How bad can it get?

Verona
I don't know. All I know is, they're biting me and my legs are really itchy! What am I going to do?

Giacomo
Don't panic. Listen to me and I'll tell you what we're going to do. I'm going back into town to get some more chemicals. While I'm gone, you take Florence outside, bathe her again and put more flea powder on her. Then tie her up outside. We don't want her inside again until all the fleas are dead.

Verona
Well, you'd better hurry – these bites are driving me insane.

Giacomo
I'll be back in no time.

Scene 7

Narrator
Giacomo heads into town to get some flea-killing chemicals. The fleas realize that their days are numbered.

Flea 1
I'd better jump out of here quick or it'll be curtains for me.

Flea 2
I'm right behind you!

Flea 1
Let's hop back to the dog. Then when Verona takes the dog outside, we can jump into the grass before Verona gets the water and the flea powder on us.

Flea 2
Good idea. Once the flea powder has worn off and they've cleaned up the house, we can jump onto the dog again and get a ride back inside where it's warm.

Collecting Things

Written by Stanley Ling

There are many small things I can collect in my hand,
Like a stretchy, bendy, brown rubber band.

There are many small things I can collect in a pot,
Like tangly twine all tied in a knot.

There are many small things I can collect in a box,
Like cogs and springs from ancient clocks.

There are many small things I can collect in my pocket,
Like a tiny, glistening, golden locket.

There are many small things I can collect in a hat,
Like the bell on the collar of my sister's cat.

There are many small things I can collect in a bag,
Like a hastily written sale-price tag.

There are many small things I can collect in a car,
Like a yummy, scrummy chocolate bar.

readingsafari.com

Check out these Safari magazines, too!

Have your say -

e-mail your Safari Tour Guide at tourguide@readingsafari.com

- Inbox
- Outbox
- Sent Mail
- Deleted
- Drafts

Subject: Very Small Things

Now you have read this magazine, is there anything you feel strongly about? E-mail your point of view to the Safari Tour Guide.

Find some fun things to do!

Go to – http://www.readingsafari.com

Safari Superstar

Name – General Phagocyte

Age – 12

Find out more about this Safari Superstar at **http://www.readingsafari.com**